# 1. What does this booklet offer?

There is no shortage of encouragement, and pressure, for teachers to improve their work, raise their standards, better their students' test scores, and so on. For the past 15 years or more the helpful part of such pressures has amounted to little more than the classic 'must try harder'. However, there have also been other voices offering advice on how to try harder, and advice of this kind has become part of government policy in recent years. Such advice amounts to telling teachers how they should do a better job, which can be offensive if it comes from those who do not share their everyday problems. Indeed, at least some of the initiatives on offer might best be seen as snake oil, in that the enthusiasm of their proponents is not matched by any evidence that they will be either feasible or effective in practice.

This booklet offers advice to teachers on how to interact more effectively with students, on a day-to-day basis, promoting their learning. What is offered is backed by rigorous evidence that the initiatives proposed do actually improve students' learning achievements. This background to the ideas is explained in section 2. The specific aim here is the improvement of science ed

our ideas are put in the context of the aims and expectations of science teaching.

The recommendations we make gain particular strength from the fact that they are grounded in the main findings of many decades of research into the principles that govern effective learning and the factors that help support the motivation and self-esteem of learners. These foundations for formative work are discussed in section 4.

Sections 5 to 8 set out in detail our findings on four main ways of practising formative assessment which we have found to be both workable and productive with science teachers.

A closing section, section 9, discusses an approach to formulating a plan to develop formative work within a science faculty in a school.

# 2. Background history

The findings on which this booklet is based have their origin in a review of research, published in 1998 both as a full article and in summary form as a short booklet for teachers (Black and Wiliam, 1998 a,b). This work established that there was strong evidence that formative assessment raise standards of pupil achievement, but that the assessment practices entailed were not implemented in most classrooms. This led the group at King's College to explore the potential for practical improvement by collaborating with a group of teachers willing to take on the risks and extra work involved, with support from their schools and their local education authorities (LEAs). Through collaboration with the Medway and Oxfordshire LEAs we were able to recruit six secondary schools, spanning a range of catchment backgrounds. At the outset, 12 science and 12 mathematics teachers were involved; 12 teachers of English joined in the work at a later stage.

The first outcomes, which took over two years to achieve, were that almost all of the teachers were positive about the effects of the project for them, and that there were significant gains in test performance for the classes involved.

On the basis of observations and records of visits to classrooms by our team, records of meetings of the whole group of teachers, interviews with and writing by the teachers themselves, and a few discussions with pupil groups, we were able to summarise the findings in a second short booklet for teachers (Black et al, 2002), and to report them at length both in a book (Black et al, 2003) and in many papers in professional and research journals.

Following that project, members of the King's College team have made numerous contributions to teachers' conferences and to school and LEA INSET training. They have also helped in developments on a larger scale, notably with the Scottish Educational Department, and with the States of Jersey. The development of formative assessment has been made a significant component of the DfES initiative for key stage 3, work towards which the King's College team are also making direct contributions.

Throughout this work, we have always been aware that formative assessment has both *generic* features, ie features which will apply to learning across all stages and all school subjects, and features which are *specific*, for example to primary teachers and to individual subjects. In this booklet, we focus on the needs and opportunities relevant to secondary science teachers, although many of the ideas are appropriate for other subject areas and for the primary classroom.

## 3. Aims of science teaching

In England, the content of science lessons is currently determined by the National Curriculum schemes of work and examination syllabuses, but there has been considerable groundswell in recent years to reshape the curriculum in science. The *Beyond 2000* report (Millar and Osborne, 1998) has set a marker for the ways in which it is hoped that the science curriculum will be approached and taught, so that it not only provides for the future scientists in our society but also educates scientifically literate citizens. A pilot study, '21st century science', is currently being trialled and developed in a number of schools.

While curricular changes may affect the approach that teachers take to science, the fundamental ideas that we try to convey to learners remain the same. Science provides the means by which learners can interact with the world around them and develop ideas about the phenomena they experience. So, when they attempt activities such as germinating seeds, their studies in science equip them with ways to observe and question what is happening. Through experiments they can begin to work out and predict what might happen if conditions for the growing plant change. To be able to learn science in this way, students need help in developing process skills to investigate, and communication skills to question and discuss findings.

Formative assessment fits well into this learning scenario, since its purpose is for teachers to sift the rich data that arise in class discussion and activity, so that professional judgements can be made about the next steps in learning. At specific times, learners also have to prepare for examinations, which currently are written. While there needs to be a focus on literacy in science to support this, there also has to be time set aside near to the end of courses to hone examination technique. Feedback, peer- and self-assessment all have important roles to play in this process and utilised properly formative assessment can result in large learning gains.

Information and communication technology (ICT) already plays a large part in science teaching and there are many good resources available, such as simulations of science processes, and data logging equipment, which allow time to focus on the thinking and theories of science. Effective formative approaches to ICT in science are still very much in their infancy but it is hoped that the potential of ICT will provide diagnostic assessment that supports learners and teachers in deciding the next steps in learning.

## 4. Principles of learning

Two types of feedback are essential to formative assessment: the first is from student to teacher, the second from teacher to student. Learning is effected by alternation between these, in which each contribution responds to the other. Thus, for classroom dialogue, the starting point is a question formulated by the teacher to help students put 'on the table' the ideas which are the starting point for them. This implements the **first** principle of learning, which is to start from where the learner is, recognising that students have to be active in reconstructing their ideas and that to merely add to those ideas an overlay of new ideas leads to poor understanding, if not to confusion.

But that is not enough: the teacher then has to encourage, and to listen carefully to, a range of responses, taking them all seriously whether they be right or wrong, to the point or zany, and helping students to talk through inconsistencies and to respond to challenges. In such discussion, the teachers are fashioning their interventions to meet the learning needs that have been made evident, but they are also implementing a **second** principle of learning, which is that students must be active in the process – learning has to be done *by* them, it cannot be done *for* them.

A **third** principle is that in order to learn, students must understand the learning target, which requires understanding of what would count as a good quality piece of work. They must also have an idea of where they stand in relation to that target. Only with these two can they achieve meta-cognition, which is the power to oversee and steer their own learning in the right direction, so that they can take

responsibility for it. This is no small achievement, and teachers need to help students understand the targets of the learning work and the criteria of quality, so that they can tell whether a product of their efforts does or does not meet the criteria. Peer- and self-assessment are essential here, for they promote both active involvement and practice in making judgements about the quality of work – both their own and that of fellow students.

**Fourthly**, when students are talking about science ideas, whether in a whole-class dialogue or in peer groups, they are using the language of science. 'Talking the talk' is an important part of learning. Teachers know that to serve their own learning, an INSET day must give them the opportunity to express their ideas and to try out ways in which new inputs might make sense to them and to their colleagues. The same is true for the learning of their students.

It is also important to think about how feedback affects the motivation and self-esteem of students. Feedback can be of two kinds. The **first kind** focuses on the student as a good or bad achiever, emphasising overall judgement by marks, grades, rank-order lists, and so on. This helps to develop what researchers have called ego-involvement, and its effects are negative. It discourages the low attainers, but it also makes high attainers avoid tasks if they cannot see their way to success, for failure would be seen as bad news about themselves rather than as an opportunity to learn. In the **second kind**, the focus is not on the person but on the strengths and weaknesses of the particular piece of work, emphasising what needs to be done to improve. This helps to develop task-involvement. Its effects are positive for it can encourage all students, whatever their past achievements, to see that they can do better by trying, and that they can learn from mistakes and failures (for the evidence, see Dweck, 1999).

# 5. Questioning and dialogue in science classrooms

Our definition of formative assessment focuses on feedback as the activity that helps learning because it provides information to be used by teachers, and by their students in assessing themselves, to modify the teaching and learning activities in which they are engaged. For feedback to be effective it needs to arise from learning experiences that provide rich evidence so that judgements about the next step in learning can be made. There are a number of ways in which this can be achieved but the essential ingredients are:

- challenging activities that promote thinking and discussion

- rich questions
- strategies to support all learners in revealing their ideas
- opportunity for peer discussion about ideas
- group or whole-class discussions which encourage open dialogue.

## *Challenging activities*

If science teachers want to find out what students understand in science rather than just what they know and can recite, then the learners need to be challenged by activities that make them think. In some cases, this would involve applying the science ideas that they already have within a new context or from a different viewpoint. In others, it would encourage the learners to use their current knowledge to predict outcomes or solve problems. These activities could take many forms in science but generally fit into the following categories:

- **Comparing**
  *What is similar and what is different about …?* (eg comparing two geranium cuttings grown in different types of soil; comparing ideas about combustion with those about respiration).

These types of activity encourage learners to observe more carefully and to find reasons for similarities and differences. By thinking about the similarities and differences, the question of why are there these similarities and differences arises. So, they apply their knowledge and understanding to the context and this both challenges their conceptual understanding and helps it develop. What is essential in these activities is that the teacher makes clear to the learners that the activity is to explore what they think rather than for them to guess the answer that the teacher has in his or her head. So if the activity is to spot the odd one out in copper, aluminium and graphite, then the teacher needs to allow the learners to discuss the various possibilities before homing in on the one that he or she wants to use to exemplify the ideas.

- **Categorising, grouping and recognising exceptions**
  *Why is … an example of …? Is it always true that …?* (eg investigating the reactions of an unknown compound; observing waterfleas to decide on their classification).

These types of activity enable learners to test out the rules and theories that they come across in science to see how generalisable they are and to recognise limits. They allow the teacher to check the reasons the learners have for allocating something to a group and to test understanding. So asking *'Is it always true that green organisms photosynthesise?'* is a better question than *'Which organisms photosynthesise?'*. This is because the first question forces the learners to ask themselves other questions to find the answer and so promotes thinking, while the second question merely looks for a recall answer.

- Predicting
  *What might happen if …?* (eg investigating leaf decay in ordinary and waterlogged soil; reasoning what implications might arise if a law forced all aircraft to have their passenger seating facing the back of the plane).

These types of activity encourage learners to apply their knowledge and understanding to future situations, through which they can then either test or reason their ideas. Again this technique encourages learners to bring their ideas to the fore and so the teacher is able to gauge what they know, what they partly know and what they do not know.

## Rich questions

Questions have a range of roles to play in the science classroom. To exploit formative opportunities it is necessary to move away from the routine of limited factual questions and to refocus attention on the quality and the different functions of classroom questions.

Collaboration between teachers to exchange ideas and experiences about good questions will be very valuable. Sometimes the science teacher needs questions to check the students' knowledge of a unit or a term or an example. These are not rich questions in that they usually result in one-word answers and are asking for facts that are known or not known rather than asking the learner to delve deep into their conceptual understanding. However, they are necessary as they help the learner to pick up the language of science. Examples are:

*What unit do I use to measure force?*
*What do we call substances that do not conduct electricity?*
*Can anyone name a type of reaction?*

More often in science we need questions that demand thinking and discussion. These are often open-ended and require learners either to link or apply ideas or give reasons why they believe something to be so. Sometimes they force the learner to ask themselves further questions to qualify what the original question is actually asking them to explain. Answers to such questions generally require one or more sentences. Examples are:

*What is similar and what is different about tapwater and seawater?*
*Why are salting, smoking and freezing all effective ways of preserving meat?*
*Why is beta radiation more dangerous than alpha radiation?*

*If plants need sunlight to grow, why aren't the largest plants found in the desert?*
*Is it always true that increasing the temperature speeds up a reaction?*
*Thinking about the particle model for solids and liquids, what do you think ice looks like at the particle level?*
*Do you think friction would be the same on the Moon as it is here on Earth?*

A rich, or big, question is one that cannot be answered immediately but rather requires the learner to work on a series of smaller questions and activities before they return to have a stab at answering it. By its nature, it encourages answers from a wide range of students, and classes should be encouraged to come up with a list of smaller questions that they will need to answer before an answer to the big question can be formulated.

For example, a rich question might be:

*Why are some forms of renewable energy more suited to some areas of the country than others?*

The smaller questions which need to be answered are:

*What is meant by renewable energy?*
*Which types of renewable energy do I know?*
*What conditions are needed for the different forms of renewable energy?*
*How might different parts of the UK differ in relation to these conditions?*

Other rich questions might be:

*How do the changes in conditions in a rockpool over a day affect what happens inside a crab?*
*How can environmental damage to ancient statues be reduced?*
*If you keep a drink with ice cubes in a thermos flask, do you need to leave room for the ice cubes to melt?*
*What would freefall be like on the Moon?*

## *Strategies to support all learners*

Through formative questioning, the teacher hopes to collect rich evidence of the students' understanding. The aim is not simply to find out what they know but also what they don't know and possibly, more importantly, what they partly know. Teaching is about helping youngsters realise this and then guiding them to upgrade their part-knowledge to a fuller understanding. It's the counterside of assessment of learning, where we can find out what students know. Formative assessment is about moving their knowledge and understanding forward and providing a means for helping students do this.

Demanding questions require time for the learner to work out an answer. For some questions and with some types of learner this can be achieved by increasing the wait time (the time between a teacher asking a question and taking an answer). Rowe (1974) found that the wait time in primary science classes was very low, less than one

second. In the secondary science classrooms that we worked in, we found that teachers could, with practice, increase their wait time to around 3–5 seconds and this had dramatic effects on the involvement of their students in classroom discussion. Our research showed that:

- longer answers were given than previously
- more students were choosing to answer
- fewer students refused to answer
- students commented on or added to the answers of other students
- more alternative explanations or examples were offered.

In many classrooms, even when the wait time is increased, there is a reluctance from some learners to offer answers. To try to engage more learners in answering, a number of techniques were developed. Some teachers forced learners to contribute by asking them to jot down an answer either on a piece of paper or on a mini-whiteboard, so that when asked by the teacher, the student would either read out or hold up their answer. Other teachers adopted a 'no hands up' strategy, taking the view that if sufficient wait time was given, then everyone should be expected to answer and so the teachers selected individuals to respond. Other teachers have used red and green cards, where learners can indicate with the green card that they know the answer, with the red card that they do not know the answer, and by showing both cards that they *might* know the answer. In this strategy, learners often changed their card as they listened to the answers of their peers, because either their own ideas were challenged or consolidated or, in some cases, a vital part of a peer's answer enabled them to complete their own thinking.

## *Opportunity for peer discussion*

Creating the classroom culture where students feel they can reveal current understanding and be helped to firmer understanding is an essential ingredient to making formative assessment function in the classroom. Peer discussion plays an important part in creating such a supportive environment. The opportunity to discuss ideas within a small group helps students articulate and check ideas before they reveal their group's answer to the whole class. Answers are better formed through the group activity, and if an answer is incorrect or limited, then it feels less threatening to the individual who offered that answer, as it is their group's decision and not theirs alone.

Concept cartoons are excellent activities to promote peer discussion since they encourage learners to work out what they do know, partly know and do not know about a specific idea or concept. By agreeing or disagreeing with the different statements on the cartoon, students provide evidence of their thinking that is less threatening and more thought-provoking than the use of direct questioning. Discussing with peers provides the vehicle to bring the learner's own ideas and thinking to the surface.

These activities can be adapted to look at most science concepts. Naylor and Keogh (2000) have produced books and CD ROM versions of concept cartoons which are useful resources for formative assessment in the science classroom.

*Concept Cartoon – Shall we put a coat on our snowman?*

## Encouraging open discussion

Students are often reluctant to commit to an answer because they do not want to reveal their inadequacies to the teacher and to their peers. The teacher's role when formative questions are asked is to act as a facilitator and encourage students to try to answer and also to listen carefully to the answers from their peers.

Sometimes questions can be used to encourage learners to reflect both on what they think and what they have heard from others. This is an essential stage in shaping understanding. Examples are:

*What can we add to Yagnesh's answer?*
*Which parts of Suzie's answer would you agree with?*
*Can someone improve on Jack's answer?*
*Where else might we find Amy's idea working?*
*Would Leon's method work in all cases?*
*What sort of evidence would challenge Sally's idea?*
*Are Sonia's and Tariq's ideas the same or different?*

This is not an easy role to play for some teachers. Learners will look to the teacher to pass judgement on answers either by comment, facial expression or body language. While it is important to sort out wrong ideas, teachers need to be patient and wait for the various ideas and thoughts to be revealed before they start correcting and curbing the direction of the discussion.

If intervention comes too soon, then not only do many of the misplaced ideas fail to be revealed but there may be too little opportunity for the learner to reflect on what is being discussed alongside what they think.

## 6. Feedback

Feedback from teachers is an essential part of assessment for learning. This can be provided orally or in writing. While many of the science teachers involved in our project looked for opportunities to increase oral feedback in their classrooms, this tended to be limited to whole-class or group feedback or occasionally to specific individuals who were in need of one-to-one attention on some aspect of their work. In the main, feedback from science teachers was through marking.

Before working on formative assessment, most of the teachers we worked with used marks to sum up students' work. This is a quick recording device for the teacher, often simply meaning 'has done the work asked and got most of it correct'. There is no sense here that learning is involved. Marks have no place in a formative environment for the following reasons:

- Learners do not get advice on how their work can be improved.

- Marks emphasise competition not personal improvement. This discourages collaborative learning.
- Marks demotivate low attainers and give no challenge to high attainers.

Teachers often compromise by using marks and comments. However, research (Butler, 1987) indicates that this is a waste of time on the teacher's part because the students focus only on the marks and fail to read the comments which could provide advice for improvement. Effective feedback should help the learners know where they are and where they should go next: the focus is improvement. Where teachers tried to achieve this using marks and comments the advice tended to be too brief and related to the reason for awarding the mark rather than improvement (eg *Excellent, More detail needed, A good effort, Write in sentences, Draw larger diagrams*).

Comments are the most common way for the teacher to have a dialogue with everyone in the class. While comments take a long time to write, the teachers we worked with found them worth making. Useful comments, written every two to three weeks, were more helpful than a mark on every piece of work. Indeed, when the teachers began devising suitable comments for specific pieces of work, they began to recognise that some activities were difficult to write comments about. If the task is to draw and label a blast furnace, then there's little to comment on and so devising an effective comment becomes difficult. Such tasks simply need checking to ensure learners have transferred the information from their textbook or the board into their own books. Checking does not usually need teacher expertise and so for this type of task, it is possible to use self-checking, peer-assessment, or sample checking by the teacher of perhaps a third of the books each week. Finding the right balance between comment-marking and checking work not only provides the time for devising useful comments, it begins to move the responsibility for involvement in assessment onto the shoulders of the learners. This is an important step towards the development and encouragement of self-assessment.

The project teachers realised that the reason why some activities were easier to comment on than others was generally because these activities were challenging and often required reasoning rather than simple recall. This led them to reassess their schemes of work to ensure that there were enough of these types of activity reasonably spaced throughout the topic. This made the marking load more manageable for the teachers and also provided regular guidance to the students while, at the same time, giving them opportunity for work on improvement before the next detailed feedback. In many cases, teachers changed some of the activities, introducing pieces that required a page or more of writing rather than tasks that rendered one-word or single-sentence answers. As with the dialogue work, this provided a richer source of evidence for the teacher to find the leading edge of learning for individual students and so provide more focused advice on their work. In some year 10 and 11 classes, essays were reintroduced so that understanding could be shown and misconceptions and errors revealed, with a view to helping sort out problems and partial knowledge. Often, the essay title encouraged the students to suggest what might happen if something was changed or to give reasons for a change that had been noticed. Examples of such titles included:

*What would happen if a villain sprayed the countryside with a chemical that destroyed chlorophyll?*

*Explain why weathering on limestone houses happens quicker in cities than in the countryside.*

*Why are some alternative energy sources more suited to Medway than to Derbyshire?*

*If you wanted to slow down the reaction between magnesium and an acid but get a steady supply of hydrogen gas, what would you do and why would you do it?*

While initially there was some resistance to the increase in writing in science, this was quickly allayed as students came to realise that these types of activity provided the starting point for the teacher to coach them towards higher attainment.

## Effective comments

Questions are useful ways of framing comments. Compare these two comments:

*Add notes on seed dispersal.*

*Can you suggest how the plant might disperse its seeds? Could this be an advantage?*

Whereas the first comment gives the student a task to perform to improve his or her work, the second comment initiates thinking immediately. This enables the learner to discuss his or her thoughts either with the teacher or a peer and its questioning nature encourages the student to initiate improvement. The first comment simply describes a deficit in the piece of work.

Targets are another effective way of giving feedback and the more focused the target the better. Try to avoid general statements as in the first example above. Points that need to be considered next time may be useful but comments that prompt immediate action, such as those below, are better.

*Work on your graphing skills.*

*Think about the accuracy and neatness when drawing graphs.*

*When you have drawn the line of best fit, check anomalous plots and decide if you have plotted them correctly or whether they really are anomalous.*

In many cases, an effective comment relates back to the success criteria or descriptions of quality that have been shared with or devised by the students before they attempt a task. In this way, students work towards success or quality by considering the criteria as their work progresses. The feedback is then the teacher's judgement which can be matched against the student's own judgement of quality. For example, suppose a student is asked to describe and explain the function of a specialised cell. What is needed is:

- a description of the cell structures that differ from a typical cell
- the life process(es) with which this cell is involved
- how the specialisation enables the cell to perform the life process better.

Effective comments that relate to these criteria might be:

*Accurate description and function of a red blood cell. Now you need to explain why having haemoglobin helps in oxygen transport.*

*Why does the root hair help the cell take up water and minerals?*

*Is it just the thinness of epithelial cells or are there further specialisations that make a group of these cells an excellent lining layer?*

*Having myelin and dendrites are nerve cell specialisations. What function do these structures help the cells with?*

Sometimes directing students where to go for help and what to do to improve can be effective.

*Look back at the way we worked out scales for graph axes and pinpoint the mistake you are making.*

*Go back to the notes we made on 30th Jan and check where chlorophyll is in the leaf and the reasons why leaves are good photosynthetic structures.*

*You are mixing up the terms power, energy and force. First check your glossary for explanations of these terms, then read pages 27–30 to see how your textbook uses power and energy correctly. Finally, see if you can rewrite this using the terms correctly.*

*Some good points made about fuels. Now you need to tie the ideas together. Take a look at how Anil has done this and ask him to help you improve this piece.*

## Creating the improving classroom

The opportunity to react to and act on comments is essential, particularly when formative ideas are being introduced to classes. The learners need to see that the teacher really does want a piece of work improved and that improvement is being monitored. This means providing an opportunity in lesson time for learners to read comments on their work and to discuss with their teacher or their peers which specific improvements are needed. In some instances, it is also useful to allow time for the improvements to be made in class.

A simple method that supports the development of improving work through comment-only marking, is to attach the top of an A4 sheet of paper into the back cover of the learner's book. Each time a piece of work is comment-marked, the learner slips the sheet between the appropriate pages of their book. The teacher adds comments onto the sheet of paper. The sheet then contains an accumulation of comments and allows both the learner and teacher to recognise where improvements have been made or where specific problems are arising. In some cases, this comment sheet becomes a written dialogue between the teacher and the learner. One teacher wrote the following comment on a piece of work where the student had been asked to describe the substances that she would encounter in a sports centre:

*Good range of substances and you know which are solids, liquids and gases. Try using the terms atom and molecule instead of particle all the time.*

The student responded with the following comment which pinpointed the learning difficulty that she was having:

*I think I've done it sir except for line 3. Can chlorine be a molecule because it's an element and I thought elements were made of the same type of atoms?*

If learners could be this precise in identifying their uncertainties, then teaching would be much simpler. Such recognition by the learner initiates the desire to sort out their uncertainty and so learning is moved forward. Feedback drives formative action.

The ultimate user of assessment information is the learner and the culture needed in the classroom to support and encourage the learner is one of success, backed by a belief that all can achieve. While this can help all students, it gives particularly good results with low attainers, where it concentrates on specific problems with their work. Comments give the learner a clear understanding of what is wrong along with appropriate targets and a means of achieving these in the short term. It is essential that the message within the feedback comment focuses on achievement and improvement of specific pieces of work to avoid such learners losing sight of their goal or being inhibited from attempting it because of overtones of ability, comparison and competition. One method of finding the correct balance and tone to encourage redrafting and further improvement is 'two stars and a wish'. For example:

*Collection and tabulation of data are both good. Now you need to explain clearly the pattern within the data.*

*Definition of osmosis is accurate and the diagram is clear. Now you need to explain how this is different from simple diffusion.*

*Circuit diagrams are clear and you can distinguish between a parallel and series circuit. Can you also explain why the bulbs are brighter in the parallel circuit?*

*Description of Haber process is correct and equation accurate. Why is that particular pressure and temperature selected to run the process?*

*Good use of examples and excellent drawing of Marram Grass TS. You need to explain carefully what adaptation is, thinking about why some individuals can survive in that harsh environment and others cannot, and the consequence of this.*

# 7. Self- and peer-assessment

Self-assessment has an essential role to play in formative practice. Teachers can create wonderful lessons by facilitating debates on ideas and providing guidance on the next learning steps but it is only the learner who can do the learning; it cannot be done for them by the teacher. In other words, students need to be able to self-assess. This is not a simple task as it requires the student to have a sufficiently clear picture of the targets in the learning trajectory ahead of them and a means of moving forward to close the learning gap. In some classrooms, students do not have this clear picture and respond to lessons as a set of exercises to be completed. In this scenario, the students are not engaged with the learning and are not aware of the rationale behind specific tasks. So, finding their way through to attain their individual targets is a non-starter. However, when students do acquire such an overview, they then become more committed and effective learners.

Through our work with teachers, we have found that peer-assessment helps students develop and hone their self-assessment skills. Students have the ability to recognise both quality and inadequacies in other students' work even if the level of competence that they themselves are performing at is different from the level of work that they are reading. With careful coaching using criteria for quality, students can begin to develop awareness of success and of problem areas in specific pieces of work and to articulate these to each other. This is clearly enhanced if the students are also regularly receiving effective guidance comments from their teacher as this provides the language, style and model to help them discuss their work with one another and provide feedback. Ideas for improvement are not isolated statements but are assimilated into the students' growing ideas about work quality, so that peer discussion enables each student to see the strengths and weaknesses of their own work with greater clarity. Such practice also encourages students to improve pieces of work as they begin to see how small changes, additions or different ways of approaching parts of the work can easily raise the quality; it is the regular small pushes forward that help embed better learning behaviours and raise overall attainment.

## Developing peer assessment

As with other formative assessment techniques, students need training, and starting in a small way and evolving their practice gradually is the best way forward. One of the science teachers with whom we worked started with simple checking of work, so once a week students swapped books and checked that axes on graphs were labelled, that measurements had

appropriate units and that the keywords for the topic had been spelt correctly. They then wrote a comment which stated at least one good point and, if possible, one aspect to look out for in future work. Once this became a regular part of practice, they moved on to looking for specific criteria in a piece of work. In an experimental report on Hooke's law, the criteria were:

- correct method including safety points and how accuracy was achieved
- table with at least five results
- line graph with accurate plots and line of best fit
- conclusion that correctly used the word proportional(ity).

Peers marked the reports and wrote a summary of their decisions about the work quality. The students then read and discussed the comments that had been written in their books. The teacher selected some students to read out the comments in their books and to say whether they agreed with their partner's judgement or not. Mostly there was agreement but when there was discrepancy, students showed specific parts of the work to others and the quality was discussed openly until a group decision was reached. Students gradually acquired the habits and skills of collaborative learning and through peer-assessment developed the objectivity required for self-assessment.

## Traffic lights

Other teachers used traffic-light icons to help develop self-assessment skills. Students labelled their work green, amber or red according to whether they thought they had good, partial or little understanding. Such a system also provides information for the teacher about individual students' confidence levels with particular ideas and topics. Clearly, if many students assign red to a piece of work, then the teacher soon realises that this is work that needs to be revisited for the students to gain a better understanding. Conversely, a plethora of greens indicates that understanding is good and the class is ready to move on to more challenging work. A mixture of reds, greens and ambers calls for different action and often teachers would pair up green and amber students to talk about the work leaving themselves free to deal with the more serious problems that the red students were having. The teacher can thus map the pace and content of future work according to the students' needs.

The traffic-light icons highlight for students areas of work where they need to make an extra effort or seek more help in developing their understanding. The icons help them actively grasp responsibility for learning and so reduce their dependency on the teacher.

In one science lesson, a teacher used the traffic-light icons and peer-assessment to help students check on their understanding at a particular point in the topic. Students were asked to revise the work completed so far for homework and in the next lesson the teacher divided the class into groups of five. The teacher then handed out sets of cards to each group. Each set had five cards which named a mini-topic from their revision: digestion, absorption, circulation, blood clotting and immunity. Each member of the group randomly selected a card and was given five minutes to prepare a talk on the mini-topic on their card. In each group, students took it in turns to explain their mini-topic to the rest of the group and the four listening students used traffic-light icons to judge how good each talk was. They used the following coding:

- green – better than I could have done and I learnt from this talk
- amber – about the same quality as I could do with all parts included and correct
- red – some parts missing or incorrect.

After all the talks had been given, each student was told by the others about the quality of their talk and this promoted discussion as red and green judgements were justified or challenged. To establish clearer understanding, the teacher asked the groups to name the mini-topics (not the students) that had been either red or green and to explain to the rest of the class why one or the other had been given. This action helped develop a shared understanding of what quality meant for each of the mini-topics. The formative action was for red or amber talks to be reworked and written up at green level. For the eight students who had been awarded green for their talk, their task was to select one of the other talks and write that up at a green level.

For some teachers, allowing students to make judgements such as these is difficult. The fear is that one student's misunderstanding will be fed to another. Teachers need to choose group members carefully and to eavesdrop on the talks and discussions of traffic-light judgements. Alongside what they pick up in the whole-class discussions, this should enable teachers to recognise such problems, and moving the learning more onto the students' shoulders allows the teacher time to intervene and sort out problems with groups as they occur.

## Investigative work

Practical work is one of the defining features of science. Most students remember vividly their early experiences in the science laboratory and their first attempts at lighting the Bunsen burner. One aspect of practical science is investigative work and this forms part of

the teacher assessment in key stage and GCSE examinations in England. Investigations involve students in using procedures such as planning, observing, measuring, analysing and evaluating as well as in more general skills such as decision making and communicating findings.

In the KMOFAP project, several of the teachers considered using formative assessment to help students develop and hone their investigative skills. However, because they felt constrained by the formal assessments for examination purposes, little was done to develop these ideas. With hindsight we can now see that there was opportunity to utilise formative assessment in investigations.

Teachers often introduce and develop investigative skills by considering individual processes or doing part-investigations as well as through whole investigations. This approach would allow the flexibility and time to build into the system better teacher feedback on an individual student's, or a group's, investigative skills. It would also provide the opportunity for groups to look at samples of their own work or the work of others, and so develop understanding of the investigative processes through peer learning and assessment.

Teachers have found that making students familiar with grade or level descriptions very helpful. To contextualise the criteria and so develop a better understanding of them, many teachers asked groups of students to look at some samples of work, reach judgements about levels and give guidance about next steps. Students were then able to keep these criteria in mind as they planned, carried out and wrote reports on their own investigations.

Certainly through those years when summative examinations are not looming, teachers should be encouraged to take a formative approach to investigative work so that the necessary self-assessment skills are in place when students come to perform their final investigations for summative purposes.

## 8. Formative use of summative tests

Considerable money and expertise has been used to develop the many summative tests that students take in schools in the UK. The teachers involved in our project used external tests, and tests they had constructed themselves using items from external tests, as tools to be employed formatively in the classroom. Some teachers stopped their habit of explaining the marking scheme when tests were returned and instead analysed the tests to see which specific questions were causing most problems for their classes. They then used the time after marking to rework the ideas behind the difficult questions and to give further examples of these for their students to try. For other test questions, where only a few students had answered incorrectly, students were told to find someone in the class who had answered correctly and get them to explain how they had arrived at their answer. The teacher dealt with serious gaps in understanding but smaller gaps could be closed through peer activity.

One teacher decided to give his class the end-of-topic test in the first lesson of the topic so that the students could inform him of what they knew, partly knew and did not know. Students then used traffic-light icons as follows:

- green – studied this topic and think I can answer this question correctly
- amber – studied this topic but not certain I can answer it correctly
- red – never studied this topic.

For some questions almost all of the students labelled them green and so the teacher decided that there was no need to teach that specific idea since the students claimed to understand it already. The teacher then planned his run of lessons to work on the red and amber ideas in the topic. This method provided him with more time to work on areas that students were unfamiliar with or that they found difficult. When the test was given at the end of the topic, the teacher found that the students had been correct in their judgements and had managed to answer the green questions, even though no lesson time had been spent on them in the weeks running up to the test. He also found that the average mark for the class had risen significantly when compared with similar classes in the same year and with the teacher's same-aged class in the previous year. Again, pace and content of the teaching was matched to students' needs and so better learning took place.

Some classes used traffic-light icons to focus revision for external tests. Students would use traffic lights on test items and then form groups to work on specific problem areas together. Others used traffic lights on examination syllabuses to help them see where they needed to put effort into the revision. Through these activities, students became involved in an active review of their work which enabled them to plan their revision for high stake tests more effectively.

# 9. Learning together: learning from others

The changes in practice recommended here are not easily made. They require changes in the ways teachers work with students, which may seem risky, and which will certainly be challenging. They will call for better resources, in terms of better questions and ideas about comments, and for evaluation of one's work. Furthermore, they may be, or be seen to be, contrary to some aspects of faculty or school policy. Indeed, what is involved is best seen as a voyage of discovery, a journey into new territories of teaching and learning. For such a voyage, one needs the support of companions.

Our experience shows that those taking on the development of formative assessment need to work in a team. That team must have a plan. The first essential for such a plan is that the team must have support from the faculty and/or the school. This may involve indulgence, to depart from some school rules on (say) frequent testing or recording of marks in students' books. However, the vital element is that the team must be helped to find time to talk with one another at length, to share experiences, successes and disappointments, and also to observe one another's classroom work. They should also have access to outside advice, whether from their LEA or from others with experience in formative work.

A first step in carrying out a plan will be an audit to determine what aspects of formative assessment are already being achieved. A next step would be to review various possible changes, and to decide which of them to try at the outset – for to attempt several new practices at once would be too demanding. The whole team might try the same activity, or different members might start with different activities. The plan should include a timetable extending over at least a year for trial and evaluation of all the various activities.

Evaluation is a vital part of any plan. This should be ongoing, in terms of mutual observation and of sharing of ideas and resources. It might also be summative at certain stages, when evidence of experience and test results of students might be collected, and perhaps supplemented by evaluation by colleagues not directly involved.

This should lead on to a final part of the plan, which is to envisage means of dissemination – to all in the faculty, and perhaps to and with other faculties for the school as a whole.

# References

Black, P.J. and Harrison, C. (2001a) Feedback in questioning and marking: the science teacher's role in formative assessment. *School Science Review*, **82**(301), 55–61.

Black, P.J. and Harrison, C. (2001b) Self- and peer-assessment and taking responsibility: the science student's role in formative assessment. *School Science Review*, **83**(302), 43–49.

Black, P. and Wiliam, D. (1998a) Assessment and classroom learning. *Assessment in Education: Principles, Policy and Practice*, **5**(1), 7–73.

Black, P., and Wiliam, D. (1998b) *Inside the Black Box*. nferNelson, London.

Black, P., Harrison, C., Lee, C., Marshall, B. and Wiliam, D. (2002) *Working inside the black box: assessment for learning in the classroom*. nferNelson, London.

Black, P., Harrison, C., Lee, C., Marshall, B. and Wiliam, D. (2003) *Assessment for learning: putting it into practice*. Open University Press, London.

Butler, R. (1987) Task-involving and ego-involving properties of evaluation: effects of different feedback conditions on motivational perceptions, interest and performance. *Journal of Educational Psychology*, **79**(4), 474–82.

Dweck, C.S. (1999) *Self-theories: their role in motivation, personality and development*. Brumer/Mazel, Hove.

Naylor, S. and Keogh, B. (2000) *Concept cartoons in science education*. Millgate House, Sandbach.

Millar, R. and Osborne, J. (1998) *Beyond 2000: science education for the future*. King's College London Department of Education and Professional Studies.

Rowe, M.B. (1974) Wait time and rewards as instructional variables, their influence on language, logic and fate control. *Journal of Research in Science Teaching*, **11**, 81–94.

## *Websites*

http://www.aaiaa.org.uk

http://www.kcl.ac.uk/education/research/kallearn.html

http://www.qca.org.uk/afl